k

Book 4

TONY LOPES

RAVETTE PUBLISHING

Licensed by PSL.

This edition first published by Ravette Publishing 2006.

Printed and bound in Malta for
Ravette Publishing Limited
Unit 3, Tristar Centre
Star Road, Partridge Green
West Sussex RH13 8RA

ISBN 10: 1-84161-237-5
ISBN 13: 978-1-84161-237-9

For Steve

THE VIDEO STORE RECOMMENDED THIS HORROR MOVIE.
THE BIOLOGY LAB
SWAMP FLIES
FROGS R' US
LOPES©...
Stoney
Email: stoneytoons@hotmail.com

I LOVE WHAT YOU'VE DONE TO THE NURSERY.
Stoney
LOPES©...
Email: stoneytoons@hotmail.com

SLOW DOWN, YOU HAVE NO GUARANTEE THEY'RE EVEN GOING TO SELL!
TAP
CHIP
CHIP
Email: stoneytoons@hotmail.com
Stoney
LOPES ©...

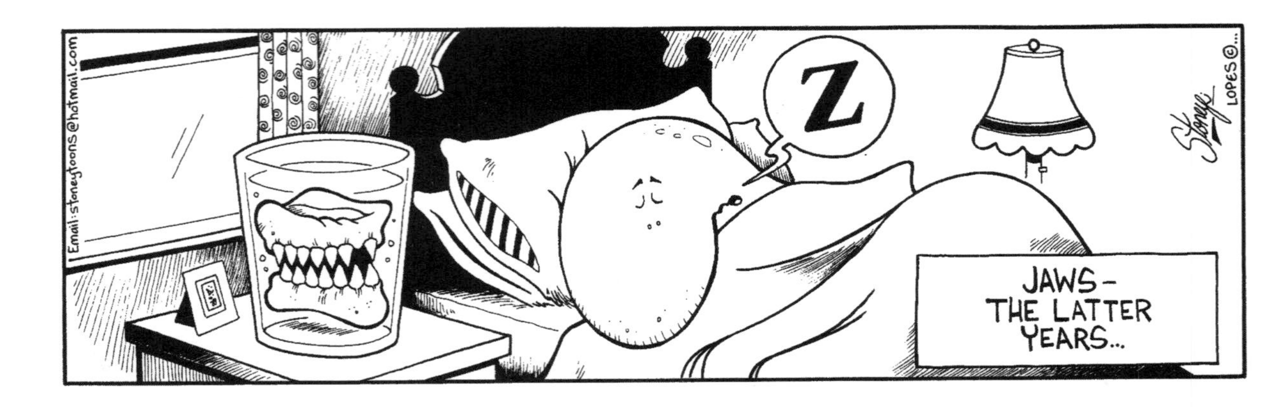
Z
JAWS - THE LATTER YEARS...
Email: stoneytoons@hotmail.com
Stoney
LOPES ©...

RIGHT TURN
ONLY
DADDY... WHO TOLD YOU HOW TO DRIVE BEFORE YOU WERE MARRIED?
Stoney
LOPES ©...
Email:stoneytoons@hotmail.com

WAH! WAH WAH WAH! WAH WAH! WAH WAH! WAH!
I'VE NEVER SEEN ANYONE SO UPSET ABOUT LOSING A COUPLE OF TEETH!
Stoney
LOPES ©...

I'M REPLACING THE ORGANIST, WHO HAS CALLED IN SICK.
St. Jude's CHURCH
TODAY: WEDDING OF PAUL and JOY
Stoney
Email: stoneytoons@hotmail.com
LOPES ©...

EXCUSE ME, WHERE IS THE FINGER FOOD?
Email: stoneytoons@hotmail.com
Stoney
LOPES ©...

CUPID'S DATING AGENCY
TO BE HONEST, I'M MORE INTERESTED IN BRAINS THAN LOOKS.
Stoney
LOPES ©...
Email: stoneytoons@hotmail.com

Email: stoneytoons@hotmail.com
FINANCIAL TIMES
FOR daddy
Stoney
LOPES ©...

STRANGE, THIS MORNING HE DIDN'T SEEM DEPRESSED.
CRIME
POLICE
BUG SPRAY
DO NOT
DO NOT CROSS PO
Stoney
Email: stoneytoons@hotmail.com
LOPES ©...

HAIR BY JOE
JUST GIVE ME A STYLE THAT'S EASY TO MAINTAIN.
Stoney
LOPES ©...
Email: stoneytoons @hotmail.com

The Greener Pastures Retirement Village
...GROWING UP, I CAN REMEMBER WHEN IN TROUBLE, MY FATHER WOULD CHASE ME AROUND THE PADDOCK WITH A MEAT TENDERISER...
LOPES ©...
Stoney
Email: stoneytoons@hotmail.com

I WAS SO WORRIED DOCTOR, LAST NIGHT HE SAID HE WASN'T IN THE MOOD!
MNQFGLI
LWTSERM
VCNOBKY
ADHJPUXZ
M.D
LOPES ©...
Stoney
Email: stoneytoons@hotmail.com

SURGERY
BEFORE WE START, CAN YOU PUT THESE ON. YOU MAY COME ACROSS A REALLY BRIGHT LIGHT!
Stoney
Email: stoneytoons@hotmail.com
LOPES ©...

R.I.P
SNOWBALL
BORN: 1992
DIED: 1994, 1996, 1997, 1997, 1999, 2000 2001, 2004 and 2006
R.I.P
R.I.P
Stoney
LOPES ©...
Email: stoneytoons@hotmail.com

NOT YOU AGAIN!
Stoney
Email: stoneytoons@hotmail.com
LOPES ©...

OH, TONIGHT YOU WANTED SOME PRIVACY, SILLY ME, I THOUGHT YOU SAID PIRACY...
Stoney
Email: stoneytoons@hotmail.com
LOPES ©...

Stoney
HUMOUR
LIBRARY
LOPES ©...
ME TARZAN - YOU HAVE GRAMMAR BOOK ?
Email: stoneytoons@hotmail.com

WHAT DID I TELL YOU BOYS ABOUT PLAYING CIRCUS ?
Stoney
Email: stoneytoons@hotmail.com
LOPES ©...

ACME CLONING CO.
IN
IN
OUT
OUT
LOPES ©...
Stoney
Email: stoneytoons@hotmail.com

15
LOPES ©...
SALE
SPAM
FOR HEAVEN'S SAKE DORIS, TELL ME THAT'S IN HERE BY MISTAKE!
Stoney
Email: stoneytoons@hotmail.com

I LIKE TO MOVE IT, MOVE IT
I LIKE TO MOVE IT, MOVE IT
YA LIKE TO "MOVE IT"
ACE MOVING CO.
LOPES ©...
Stoney
Email: stoneytoons@hotmail.com

SO, YOU FEEL THAT BEING A MECHANIC HAS TAKEN OVER YOUR LIFE.
LOPES ©...
Stoney
Email: stoneytoons@hotmail.com

LOPES ©...

STOP COMPLAINING, NORA. YOU KNOW WE CAN'T AFFORD A CAR WITH AIRBAGS!
Stoney
Email: stoneytoons@hotmail.com

C'MON HONEY, WE'RE LATE!! JUST PUT YOUR FACE ON IN THE CAR!
Stoney
Email: stoneytoons@hotmail.com
LOPES ©...

MISS HUCKLEBERRY, HAS THE TELEPHONE SYSTEM BEEN REPAIRED YET?
Email: stoneytoons@hotmail.com
Stoney
LOPES ©...

OKAY, WHICH OF YOU IS THE NEW GUY?
Stoney
Email: stoneytoons@hotmail.com
LOPES ©...

I LOVE THESE, THEY GIVE US SUCH A NICE SMOKEY FLAVOUR.
Email: stoneytoons@hotmail.com
Stoney
LOPES ©...

Snowman Humour...
Melt Me
GIGGLE
Email: stoneytoons@hotmail.com
Stoney
LOPES ©...

TRY THAT ONE MORE TIME, AND ITS THE TOILET BOWL FOR YOU!
FISH FOOD
LOPES ©...
Email: stoneytoons@hotmail.com

CAREERS ADVISOR
I WOULDN'T CONSIDER A CAREER AS A PSYCHIC, THERE'S NO FUTURE IN IT.
A-C
D-G
LOPES ©...
Email: stoneytoons@hotmail.com

YOU LICK, I'LL DRY.
Email: stoneytoons@hotmail.com
Stoney LOPES ©...

DRIVE THRU
1 COMBO
2 Combo
3 COMBO
4 COMBO
5 COMBO
Burger BARN
NO THANKS, I'M JUST BROWSING
Email: stoneytoons@hotmail.com
Stoney LOPES ©...

PEOPLE SAY TO FOLLOW YOUR GUT INSTINCT, BUT WHICH ONE?
Stoney
LOPES©...
Email:stoneytoons@hotmail.com

NANOOK'S REAL ESTATE OFFICE
OPEN
SOLD
SOLD
Stoney
LOPES©...
Email:stoneytoons@hotmail.com

BEAUTIFUL CLOTHES FOR ELEPHANT WOMEN
YOU IDIOT... I SAID ELEGANT!
Email: stoneytoons@hotmail.com
Stoney
LOPES ©...

THIS STONE WAS LAID BY the Hon Prime Minist
OOH... THAT'S GOTTA HURT!
LOPES ©...
Email: stoneytoons@hotmail.com
Stoney

LOPES ©...
WHAT DO YOU RECOMMEND FOR REALLY DRY SCALP?
PHARMACY
PRESCRIPTION DROP-OFF
Stoney
Email: stoneytoons@hotmail.com

HELLO, RECEPTION? THIS IS ROOM 115, CANCEL MY MORNING PAPER... I'LL FETCH IT MYSELF.
LOPES ©...
Stoney
Email: stoneytoons@hotmail.com

SORRY, WE SOLD OUT OF TODAY'S PAPYRUS
Stoney
LOPES©...
Email: stoneytoons@hotmail.com

SORRY IF I'M A LITTLE NERVOUS... I'M NOT USED TO FLYING.
Stoney
LOPES©...
Email: stoneytoons@hotmail.com

JUST ONE CHOPSTICK PLEASE... I'M ON A DIET.
HOUSE OF BLING BLING
Email: stoneytoons@hotmail.com
Stoney
LOPES©...

THE OLD LADY DOESN'T LIVE HERE ANYMORE, SHE MOVED INTO A PAIR OF SANDLES ON THE COAST.
LOPES©...
Email: stoneytoons@hotmail.com
Stoney

LOPES ©...
Email: stoneytoons@hotmail.com

On the town with DUNG BEETLES...
COMPLIMENTS OF THE GENTLEMAN AT THE END OF THE BAR
LOPES ©...
Email: stoneytoons@hotmail.com

HMM, YOUR FALSETTO WAS A LITTLE HIGH PITCHED, AND YOU COULD USE A LOWER BARITONE, BUT ALL IN ALL, NOT A BAD CALL.
LOPES©...
Email: stoneytoons@hotmail.com
Stoney

GEORGE!! THE FINKLESTEIN'S WILL BE HERE ANY MINUTE FOR DINNER, AND YOU'RE NOT EVEN DRAWN PROPERLY!!
LOPES©...
Stoney
Email: stoneytoons@hotmail.com

I THINK IT'D BE LOVELY IF WE KNOCKED DOWN A COUPLE OF THESE BARS... IT WOULD REALLY OPEN UP THE PLACE.
Stoney
Email: stoneytoons@hotmail.com
LOPES ©...

CRACKERS, I WANT CRACKERS!
I'VE FALLEN IN LOVE WITH GARFIELD...
SPIT COVERED TENNIS BALLS, I NEED SPIT COVERED TENNIS BALLS!
I FANTASIZE ABOUT FINDING NEMO!
Desperate Housepets
Stoney
Email: stoneytoons@hotmail.com
LOPES ©...

CLOSED
FOR LUNCH
Stoney
Email:stoneytoons@hotmail.com
LOPES©...

MUM, HOW DO I FLUSH IN HERE ?
Email:stoneytoons@hotmail.com
Stoney
LOPES©...

HI, YOU MUST BE MY BLIND DATE, HARRY...
...And thus, the career of Harry Houdini, escape artist begins...
Stoney
Email: stoneytoons@hotmail.com
LOPES ©..

PLEASE TAKE ONE
Stoney
Email: stoneytoons@hotmail.com
LOPES ©..

CAN YOU EXPLAIN THE STATE OF THIS ROOM YOUNG MAN?
BILLY'S STY
Stoney
Email: stoneytoons@hotmail.com

TIME MACHINE WORLD
IT'S OUR LATEST MODEL... AND AS A SPECIAL OFFER, YOU CAN BUY NOW AND PAY LAST YEAR!
Stoney. LOPES ©...
Email:stoneytoons@hotmail.com

HOW LONG WITH THIS HEADACHE OF YOURS? DON'T YOU REALISE OUR ENTIRE SPECIES IS ON THE VERGE OF EXTINCTION!
Email: stoneytoons@hotmail.com
LOPES ©...
Stoney

ACTUALLY NO, HE DIDN'T LOOK LIKE THAT AT ALL!
DETECTIVE BUREAU
SKETCH ARTIST
PICASSO'S little known "SKETCH ARTIST PERIOD" was short lived...
Stoney
LOPES ©...
Email: info@stoneytoons.com

MR. BOTCH WANTS TO KNOW IF THE SIGN WILL FADE OVER TIME.
ALMO'S SIGN WRITING CO.
THE WORLD WILL END TODA
Stoney
Email: stoneytoons@hotmail.com
LOPES ©...

EVERYONE, CALM DOWN, WE DIDN'T HEAR HUFFING AND PUFFING, IT'S JUST THE WIND!
Stoney
Email: stoneytoons@hotmail.com
LOPES ©...

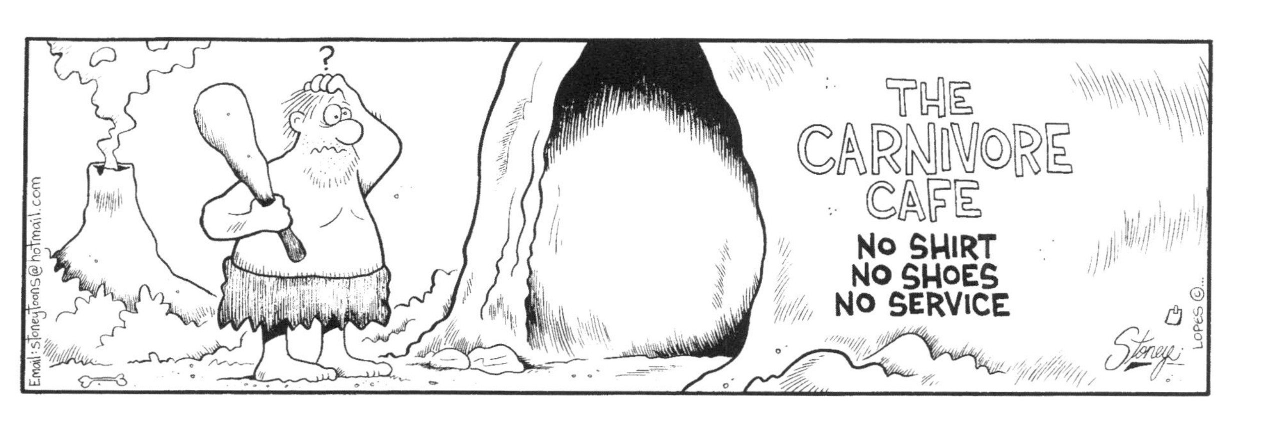
?
THE CARNIVORE CAFE
NO SHIRT
NO SHOES
NO SERVICE
Stoney
LOPES ©...
Email: stoneytoons@hotmail.com

DO YOU DO REQUESTS?
Stoney
LOPES ©...
Email: stoneytoons@hotmail.com

The overly optimistic Eskimo...
Stoney
Email: stoneytoons@hotmail.com
LOPES ©...

LOPES ©...
THIS PORK CHOP, HAS IT BEEN SITTING HERE FOR A FEW DAYS?
RUMP STEAK,
Stoney
Email: stoneytoons@hotmail.com

GOOD LORD! IT'S MY WIFE!! QUICK, TAKE OFF YOUR CLOTHES!
Stoney
LOPES ©...
Email: stoneytoons@hotmail.com

EVERYBODY SING, IF YOU'RE HAPPY AND YOU KNOW IT CLAP YOUR HANDS...
CLAP
CLAP
Stoney
Email: stoneytoons@hotmail.com
LOPES ©...

ACE LOUD HAILER CO.
MISS FASULLO, WILL YOU STEP INTO MY OFFICE PLEASE
Stoney
LOPES ©...
Email: stoneytoons@hotmail.com

DO YOU HAVE A MINT? I HAVE THAT JUST DEVOURED A POLLUTED CITY TASTE IN MY MOUTH!
Stoney
Email: stoneytoons@hotmail.com
LOPES ©...

JUST REMEMBER, I DON'T LIKE LOSING!
1
Stoney
LOPES ©...
Email: stoneytoons@hotmail.com

HIYA TOOTS! WHAT'S YOUR SIGN? CAN I BUY YOU A DRINK? HOW ABOUT A SMOOCH?
MUM SAID THERE'D BE KNIGHTS LIKE THIS!
BAR
Stoney
LOPES ©...
Email: stoneytoons@hotmail.com

Bob's
BALLOON
Shop
OPEN
LOPES ©...
Email: stoneytoons@hotmail.com
Stoney

TRY OUR VITAMINS–
YOU WON'T GET BETTER!
B+
C
B2
Stoney
Email: stoneytoons@hotmail.com
LOPES ©...

FOR GOD SAKE MAN! WILL YOU QUIT SINGING THE THEME FROM GILLIGANS ISLAND!
S O S
LOPES ©...
Email: stoneytoons@hotmail.com

IT'S ANOTHER NUISANCE CALL, SHALL I TELL YOUR MOTHER TO CALL BACK LATER?
LOPES ©...
Email: stoneytoons@hotmail.com

ANNUAL APATHY SOCIETY CONVENTION
CANCELLED DUE TO LACK OF RESPONSE
Email: stoneytoons@hotmail.com
Stoney
LOPES ©...

WE REALLY NEED TO SPEAK WITH SOMEONE ABOUT OUR PREGNANCY, -I GUESS AN OBSTETRICIAN, OR SHOULD IT BE A FISHMONGER?
Email: stoneytoons@hotmail.com
Stoney
LOPES ©...

OF COURSE I REMIND YOU OF SOMEONE - I'M YOUR WIFE!
HIC
HIC
Stoney
LOPES ©...
Email: stoneytoons@hotmail.com

DON'T YOU MISS THE GOOD OLD DAYS WHEN HE'D FETCH THE PAPER FROM THE FRONT LAWN.
DAILY NEWS
LOADING
Stoney
Email: stoneytoons@hotmail.com
LOPES ©...

Stoney
NEWS
-AND NOW OVER TO OUR WEATHERMAN WHO'S NEVER WRONG, ITS RUEBEN WITH YESTERDAY'S WEATHER
Email: stoneytoons@hotmail.com
LOPES ©...

Email: stoneytoons@hotmail.com
FOR HEAVEN'S SAKE, STAY AWAY FROM CARS!
Stoney
LOPES ©...

BAD NEWS MR. TAIT... YOU HAVE AN EYE INFECTION
Email: stoneytoons@hotmail.com
Stoney
LOPES©...

PLEASE HELP. CARDS STACKED AGAINST ME!
Email: stoneytoons@hotmail.com
Stoney
LOPES©...

VET
MY DOG DOESN'T SEEM TO BE DOING SO WELL.
Stoney
LOPES ©...
Email:stoneytoons@hotmail.com

UROLOGY DEPT.
I KEEP GOING WEE WEE WEE ALL THE WAY HOME.
Stoney
LOPES ©...
Email:stoneytoons@hotmail.com

MATERNITY
LOPES ©...
Stoney
Email: stoneytoons@hotmail.com

YOU KNOW ADAM, YOU'RE NOT THE ONLY ONE WHO WEARS THE PLANTS IN THIS RELATIONSHIP!
LOPES ©...
Stoney
Email: stoneytoons@hotmail.com

NOW THAT I CAN WALK AND TALK, I HAVE TO SIT DOWN AND SHUT UP.
Email: stoneytoons@hotmail.com
Stoney
LOPES ©...

I WONDER IF HUMAN BABIES KICK LIKE OURS?
Email: stoneytoons@hotmail.com
Stoney
LOPES ©...

HARRY JUST LOVES PLAYING IN THE BACKYARD WITH THE KIDS...
LOPES ©...
Email: stoneytoons@hotmail.com

THE NICE PARKING OFFICER LEFT ME A COMPLIMENT, IT SAYS "PARKING FINE"
LOPES ©...
Email: stoneytoons@hotmail.com

Stoney
SURE! I LOVE BEING CLOSE TO NATURE, THE FRESH AIR, BREATHTAKING VIEWS AND ALL THAT... BUT I'M REALLY HERE CAUSE MY GIRLFRIEND SAID TO GO TAKE A HIKE!
LOPES ©...
Email: stoneytoons@hotmail.com

OPEN A LITTLE WIDER PLEASE...
LOPES ©...
Stoney
Email: stoneytoons@hotmail.com

REMEMBER THE GOOD OLD DAYS WHEN THERE WERE JUST POSTMEN, AND NONE OF THIS EMAIL NONSENSE?
RECORD NUMBERS USING EMAIL
Stoney
LOPES ©...
Email: stoneytoons@hotmail.com

OOOH, YOU'RE RIGHT, HE DOES LOOK LIKE YOU!
Stoney
LOPES ©...
Email: stoneytoons@hotmail.com

HA·HA·HA
YOU BLINKED!!
Staring Death in the Face...
Stoney LOPES©
Email: stoneytoons@hotmail.com

WE'RE LIVE AT THE SCENE WHERE AUTHORITIES ARE INVESTIGATING THIS UNFORTUNATE INCIDENT INVOLVING HUMPTY DUMPTY. THE QUESTION NOW REMAINS- DID HE FALL OR WAS HE PUSHED?
CRIME SCENE
DO NOT CROSS
Stoney LOPES ©
Email: stoneytoons@hotmail.com

Email:stoneytoons@hotmail.com
SNACKS
DRINKS
WAIT A MINUTE HERB, I SHOULD HAVE THE EXACT CHANGE...
LOPES ©...

SALE
I'M AFTER A SWEATER... PREFERABLY WOOL!
Email: info @ stoneytoons.com
LOPES ©...

VERY ODD, LAWYERS NORMALLY DON'T HAVE ONE OF THESE...
LOPES ©
Stoney
Email: info@stoneytoons.com

HMM, NOT BAD, TASTES LIKE BRIAN...
Stoney
LOPES ©
Email: info@stoneytoons.com

IT'S BEEN A LOVELY EVENING, ETHEL.
I'D LIKE TO SEE YOU AGAIN IN SIX MONTHS.
the trouble with dating a dentist
Stoney
LOPES ©...
Email : info@stoneytoons.com

SALE
LOPES ©...
HOW ABOUT THIS ONE?
18
CARROTS
FOR HEAVEN'S SAKE! JUST PICK ONE AND LET'S GO!
Stoney
Email: info@stoneytoons.com

While on his honeymoon, Ronald makes a serious faux pas...
SURE, I'LL RUB SUNSCREEN ON YOUR BACK...
Stoney LOPES ©...
Email: info @ stoneytoons.com

BOOK PUBLISHERS
WITCHES Cook Book
HAS IT BEEN SPELL CHECKED?
Stoney LOPES ©...
Email: info @stoneytoons. com

...SO I SAID PULL THE UDDER ONE...
hee
hee
hee
HA-HA-HO-HA-HA-HO
STAND-UP COWMEDIAN
LOPES©...
Stoney
Email: info@stoneytoons.com

LOPES©...
Nanook and Kirima enjoy the comforts of climate control...
Stoney
Email: info@stoneytoons.com

MEET THE AUTHOR OF LIVING WITH TEENAGERS
SOB
SOB
SOB
Email: info@stoneytoons.com
LOPES ©...

HMM, YOU HAVE A SERIOUS PROBLEM WITH THE INSIDE OF YOUR BODY, PLUS, THAT PUMPY THING SEEMS TO BE BLOCKING THAT SQUISHY GOOEY PART.
- WE BETTER RUN SOME MORE TESTS...
LOPES ©...
Email: info@stoneytoons.com

LOPES ©...
Stoney
Email: info@stoneytoons.com

YOU BETTER KEEP 'EM COMING, I'M DRINKING TO FORGET!
Stoney
LOPES ©...
Email: info@stoneytoons.com

ARE YOU LEAVING?
Stoney and Lorena LOPES ©...

HONEY WAIT! YOU FORGOT YOUR MOISTURISER!
SNOOT
hee hee
HA-HA HOHO
hee hee
LOPES ©...
Stoney
Email: info@stoneytoons.com

IT APPEARS TO READ - "MUMMIFICATION FOR DUMMIES"
Email: info@stoneytoons.com
Stoney
LOPES ©...

ONE HOUR PHOTO
OPEN
I'D PREFER THIS ROLL PRINTED IN BLACK & WHITE
LEAVE FILM HERE
Email: info@stoneytoons.com
Stoney
LOPES ©...

THE CUTLETS WILL BE FINE...
Menu
MARY HAD A LITTLE LAMB
Stoney
LOPES ©...
Email: info@stoneytoons.com

INSTITUTE of MAGIC
TEST TODAY
HMM... HOW DO YOU SAW A WOMAN IN HALF?
THIS MUST BE A TRICK QUESTION...
LOPES ©...
Stoney
Email: info@stoneytoons.com